Robins
and
Rabbits

Robins
and
Rabbits

by John Hawkinson

Albert Whitman and Company
Chicago, Illinois

To Anne

There is a little rabbit
who lives in the woods.

Turtles and toads,

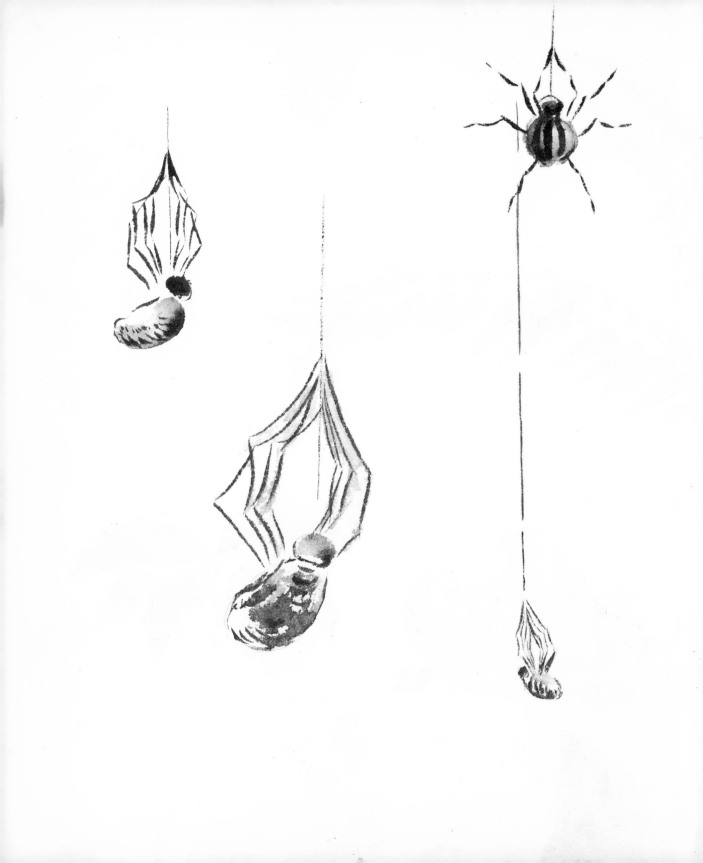

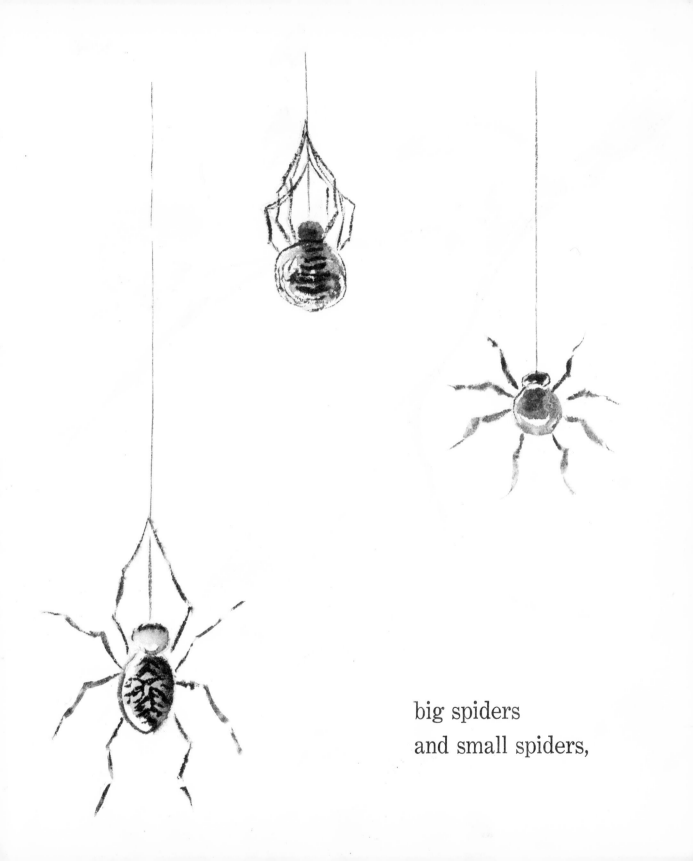

big spiders
and small spiders,

frisky squirrels,

chipmunks,

and black-capped chickadees
live in the woods.

There are graceful deer

and tiny deer mice,

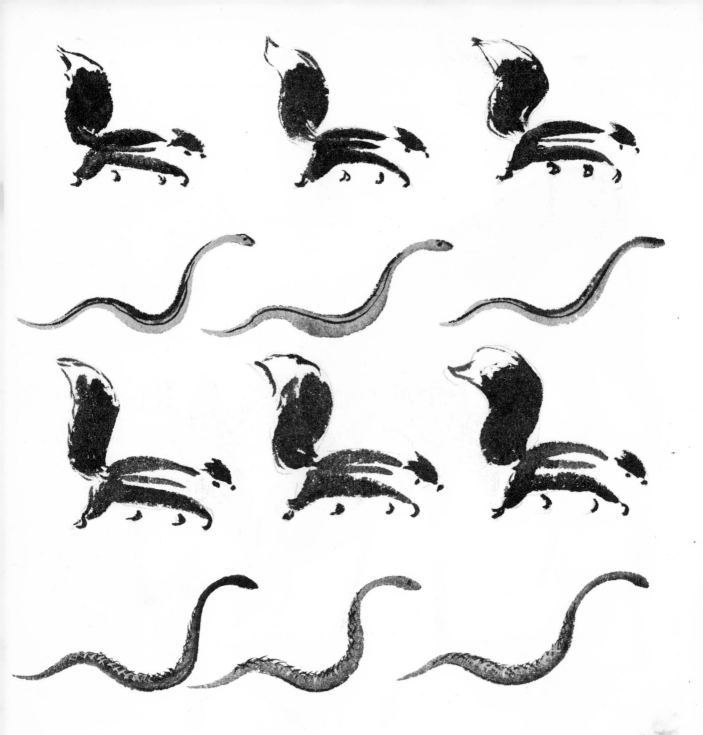

skunks and snakes,

red fox and grey fox
who live in the woods.

Bull frogs

and little frogs sing in the pond.

Fish swim in the creek,

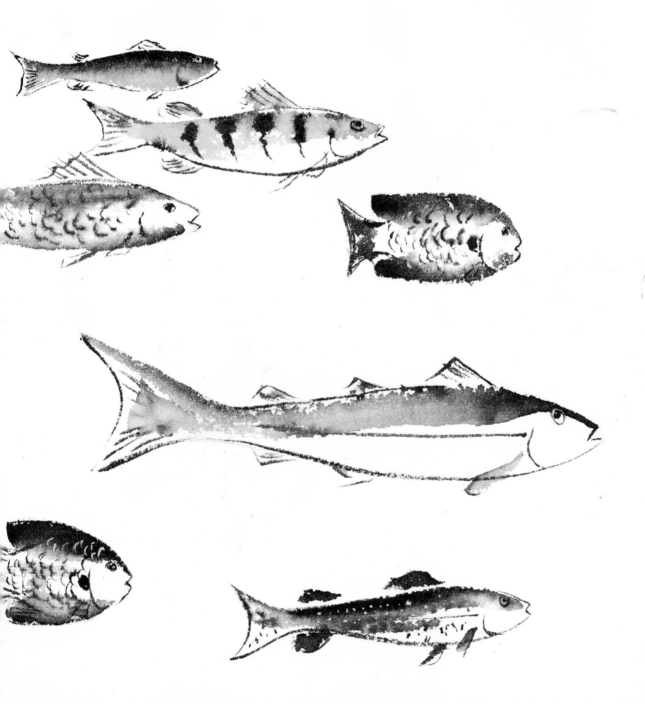

and butterflies dance in the air.

There are three brown owls,

one sleepy bear,

and many, many robins
who live in the woods.

But, in all the woods,
you can clearly see
more rabbits than robins.
For the little rabbit
who lives in the woods
has so many

brothers and sisters and cousins

and uncles and aunts!